The Little
YORKSHIRE
QUIZ
BOOK

H
HANDSTAND PRESS

Published by Handstand Press
East Banks, Dent, Sedbergh. Cumbria.
LA10 5QT

www.handstandpress.co.uk

First Published in 2014

Designed and set by Russell Holden, Pixel Tweaks, Cumbria
Graphic Artwork by Sophie Bennett, Ulverston, Cumbria
Printed in Great Britain by Short Run Press, Exeter, Devon

ISBN: 978-0-9576609-3-9

Contents

General Knowledge 1 1
History..3
Traditions...5
Food and Drink 7
Famous People 1 9
Football...11
York 13
Authors and Poets 15
Dialect and Sayings 17
The Great Outdoors 19
Houses and Gardens...21
Art 23
Leeds...25
Transport...27
Cricket...29
General Knowledge 2 31
Museums and Attractions...................................33
Buildings...35
The Ridings...37
Famous People 2 39
Sheffield..41
Name the place 43
Music..45
Industry...47
Sport...49
Hull 51
Animals...53
The Coast..55
Dales...57
TV and Film 59

How the Quiz Works

There are 30 sets of questions with answers on the following page. Unless otherwise stated, all questions relate to Yorkshire as defined by its ceremonial borders rather than modern-day local authority boundaries.

The Little Yorkshire Quiz Book is the second in our series of County Quiz Books.
Also available online or from your local bookshop,
The Little Cumbria Quiz Book.
(978-0-957-6609-1-5)

General Knowledge 1

1. When is Yorkshire Day?

2. Which of these counties does not border Yorkshire: Cumbria, Northumberland or Lincolnshire?

3. What much-loved Yorkshire item is celebrated on the first Sunday in February?

4. At the last Census in 2011, what was the approximate population of the Yorkshire and Humber region: 4.3 million, 5.3 million or 6.3 million people?

5. What links Esteli in Nicaragua, Anshan in China, Donetsk in Ukraine and Pittsburgh in the US?

6. 'Fortune Favours the Brave' is the motto of which Yorkshire institution?

7. When its makers released a Yorkshire edition of the Monopoly game, which two major buildings equated to Mayfair and Park Lane as the most expensive squares on the board?

8. Which Yorkshire town has a Royal Pump Room and Stinking Well?

9. What hillside feature near Kilburn is the largest of its kind in England?

10. According to a survey by Defra, approximately how many sheep does Yorkshire have: 1.2 million, 2.2 million or 3.2 million?

Questions

General Knowledge 1

1. **August 1st.** It was first held in 1975 a year after the realignment of county boundaries split up the traditional Yorkshire.

2. **Northumberland.** It is separated by the modern county of Durham.

3. **Yorkshire Pudding.** Yorkshire Pudding Day was first marked in 2008.

4. **5.3 million people.** It is a 6% increase on the total at the last Census in 2001.

5. **They are all twin towns of Sheffield.** Some were chosen because they have similar industrial profiles.

6. **The Yorkshire Regiment.** It is the only regiment in the army to be named after a county.

7. **York Minster and Castle Howard.** The game caused some controversy with its rankings of the worth of places and properties.

8. **Harrogate.** It was one of the 19th century's largest spa towns.

9. **The white horse**. At nearly 100m wide it was constructed by a landowner to be bigger than versions elsewhere in the country.

10. **2.2 million.** There are also 14 million chickens, 1.3 million pigs and 550,000 cattle.

Answers

History

1. What was the Romans' name for York?

2. And what did the Vikings call it?

3. Who was the Roman emperor crowned in York in 306 – the only Emperor to be crowned outside of Rome?

4. Near which village are the ancient monuments including henges and burial grounds that date back at least 5,000 years?

5. Where were the two major battles of Yorkshire in 1066 between England's army and the Vikings?

6. Which abbey, still used, was the first to be built by the Normans in Yorkshire in 1069?

7. Who was born in York and died a rather violent death in London in 1606?

8. Which castle was besieged by Oliver Cromwell's men in the civil war for three years?

9. Which Yorkshire city saw more than 1,200 people killed and 95% of its homes damaged during the Second World War?

10. In what year were the Ridings abolished as administrative regions?

Questions

History

1. **Eboracum.** The Romans founded York as a fortress in 71 AD.

2. **Jorvik.** The Vikings captured York in 866.

3. **Constantine.** There is a statue of him outside York Minster.

4. **Thornborough**. The Thornborough Henges are sometime called 'The Stonehenge of the north'.

5. **Fulford and Stamford Bridge.** They took place within a few days of each other, a couple of weeks before the Battle of Hastings.

6. **Selby Abbey.** Its patron saint is St. Germain, a 4th century French saint.

7. **Guy Fawkes.** He was born on Stonegate, and the adjacent High Petergate has a Guy Fawkes Inn.

8. **Skipton Castle**. It was the Royalists' last bastion in the north of England.

9. **Hull**. After London, it was the most badly damaged UK city in the Second World War.

10. **1974.** It caused much protest, and the Yorkshire Ridings Society, set up to preserve the historic boundaries, was founded a year later.

Answers

Traditions

1. Which colliery-inspired World Championship event is held in Gawthorpe near Ossett every year?

2. In which city has an official hornblower sounded a horn at 9pm every night for at least 1,100 years?

3. What annual activity does the village of Scorton in north Yorkshire claim is the world's longest running sporting event?

4. Market Weighton has an annual Giant Bradley Day to commemorate William Bradley, Britain's tallest ever man. With three inches either side, how tall was he?

5. What lively tradition still takes place in many Yorkshire towns before Bonfire Night each year on 4th November?

6. The Slaithwaite annual Moonraking Festival is named after 19th century men who claimed when questioned to be raking the moon from a nearby canal. What were they actually hiding there?

7. What is unusual about the Kiplingcotes Derby, the annual horse race staged in the village of Kiplingcotes near Market Weighton?

8. When was the Great Yorkshire Show first held: 1838, 1858 or 1878?

9. The Hepworth Feast is staged every June to commemorate the end of what dreadful event?

10. What is the sharp-edged traditional team dance still commonly found in Yorkshire?

Questions

Traditions

1. **The World Coal Carrying Championships.** Competitors must carry 50kg sacks of coal for just under one mile.

2. **Ripon.** It is one of the longest continually running traditions in the world.

3. **The Scorton Silver Arrow.** An archery competition using traditional bows, it has been held every year outside of wars since 1673.

4. **Seven feet nine inches.** He toured for a while under the alias of the Yorkshire Giant.

5. **Mischief Night** – otherwise known as Miggy Night, Trick Night, Tick-Tack Night or Goosey Night. It is particularly prominent in Yorkshire because Guy Fawkes was born here.

6. **Alcohol.** The modern-day festival sees locals build a giant moon and lanterns.

7. **It is reckoned to be the oldest horse race in England.** It has been held every year since 1519.

8. **1838.** It was first staged in York but now has its own showground near Harrogate.

9. **The Great Plague.** Hepworth was said to be the place furthest north of London reached by the plague.

10. **The Long Sword Dance.** A variation on it is also popular in Northumberland.

Answers

Food and Drink

1. Which town is famous for its liquorice production?

2. In what town are both Sam Smith and John Smith beers still brewed?

3. The Yorkie was just one of the bars created by which York-based chocolate manufacturer?

4. And which other York chocolatier's launches included the Chocolate Orange and All Gold?

5. What is a Fat Rascal?

6. Which Yorkshire cheese was the favourite of animated duo Wallace and Gromit?

7. What vegetable is heavily grown in a triangle of land between Wakefield, Leeds and Bradford?

8. Which of these three is NOT the name of a brewery in Yorkshire? Black Dog, Brown Cow, White Cat?

9. Which famous takeaway brand opened its first shop in Yeadon near Leeds in 1928?

10. Which delicacy, according to a character in JB Priestley's *Good Companions*, should be "eaten by itsen and not mixed up with wi' meat and potaters, all in a mush"?

Food and Drink

1. **Pontefract.** It celebrates its association with a Liquorice Festival every summer.

2. **Tadcaster.** They date back to the 18th century there.

3. **Rowntree's.** It was founded in the city in 1862 and still produces bars there.

4. **Terry's.** Its York history dates back to 1767 but it has no presence in the city now.

5. **A type of tea cake, scone or bun.** It is popular in Yorkshire but little known beyond.

6. **Wensleydale.** Wallace and Gromit now adorn the products of the Wensleydale Creamery.

7. **Rhubarb.** The soil in the area is particularly suited to its production.

8. **White Cat.** Black Sheep brews in Masham and Brown Cow in Selby.

9. **Harry Ramsden's.** The company caused huge local controversy when it closed the shop in 2011.

10. **Yorkshire Pudding.** It was traditionally served in Yorkshire before the main course rather than with it.

Answers

Famous People 1

1. Three Prime Ministers were born in Yorkshire. Can you name two of them?

2. What is the name of the current Archbishop of York, appointed in 2005?

3. Which famous Yorkshireman was born in Marton in 1728 and took up an apprenticeship in the shipping village of Staithes?

4. What organization did Settle-born Benjamin Waugh help to found?

5. Which York-based manufacturer did readers of the York Evening Press name 'Man of the Millennium' in 2000?

6. Which famous villain was hanged on the Knavesmire in York?

7. Who is the only one of these three knighted actors NOT born in Yorkshire: Sir Patrick Stewart, Sir Derek Jacobi or Sir Ben Kingsley?

8. And who is the only one of these three damed actresses NOT born in Yorkshire: Dame Judi Dench, Dame Diana Rigg or Dame Helen Mirren?

9. Which Yorkshire-born scientist's many achievements included the discovery of laughing gas?

10. Which Yorkshire-born astronaut was the first British woman in space and the first ever woman on the Mir space station?

Questions

Famous People 1

1. **Charles Wentworth, born near Rotherham; Herbert Henry Asquith, born in Morley; and Harold Wilson, born in Cowlersley.**

2. **John Sentamu**. He is fond of saying that one of his middle names, Mugabi, sounds out 'eeh by gum' if spelt backwards.

3. **Captain James Cook.** It was in Staithes that he is thought to have first discovered his love for the sea.

4. **The National Society for the Prevention of Cruelty to Children** (NSPCC).

5. **Joseph Rowntree.** He was the founder of the Rowntree's chocolate empire and also a great philanthropist.

6. **Dick Turpin.** He was buried in St George's churchyard in the city.

7. **Sir Derek Jacobi**. Stewart was born in Mirfield and Kingsley in Scarborough.

8. **Helen Mirren.** Dench was born in York and Rigg in Doncaster.

9. **Joseph Priestley.** His other firsts included the dissolving of carbon dioxide into water to create fizzy drinks.

10. **Helen Sharman.** She was born in Sheffield. At 27 she was also the fifth youngest person ever to fly in space.

Answers

Football

1. As of the 2014-15 season, Yorkshire had 11 teams in the top four divisions of England's league. Can you name them all?

2. Which Yorkshire football team has been champion of the country's top division most times?

3. Which is the longest continually established football league club in Yorkshire?

4. When was the last year a Yorkshire club won the top division?

5. Which Yorkshire side has won the FA Cup the most times?

6. A Yorkshire club has been runner-up in the FA Cup four times but won it only once. Which?

7. Two players share the honour of most appearances for Leeds United. Who are they?

8. Which club plays at Oakwell?

9. Which club is nicknamed the Bantams, and which the Millers?

10. Who is England's highest capped Yorkshire-born footballer?

Questions

Football

1. **Barnsley, Bradford City, Doncaster Rovers, Huddersfield Town, Hull City, Leeds United, Middlesbrough, Rotherham United, Sheffield United, Sheffield Wednesday and York City.**

2. **Sheffield Wednesday.** It has won the league four times. Huddersfield Town and Leeds United have each won it 3 times.

3. **Also Sheffield Wednesday.** It was founded in 1867. One of the city's non-league teams, Sheffield FC, was founded in 1857 and is widely considered the world's oldest standalone club. Yorkshire's next oldest league clubs are Middlesbrough (1876) and Doncaster Rovers (1879).

4. **1992.** Leeds United won the title this year, which was the last time the league was known as the First Division before the Premier League was born.

5. **Sheffield United.** It won the cup in 1899, 1902, 1915 and 1925.

6. **Huddersfield Town.** Its sole victory came in 1922.

7. **Jack Charlton & Billy Bremner.** They each appeared 773 times.

8. **Barnsley.** It has been the club's ground since 1887.

9. **Bradford City and Rotherham United.** Bradford are the Bantams, a name derived from the team's colours. The Millers are Rotherham, who played at a ground called Millmoor until 2008.

10. **David Seaman.** He was born in Rotherham in 1963 and made 75 appearances for England.

Answers

York

1. Which of these three York gate names is made up: Jubbergate, Whipmawhopmagate, Flibbertygate?

2. What are Mad Alice, The Headless Earl, The Grey Lady and The Lady of The Golden Fleece?

3. York offers visitors an array of historic guided tours. Which one of these three subjects is NOT offered as a tour: graveyards, toilets or waste collection?

4. What is the name of the play cycle performed in York since medieval times, often by guilds of trades and crafts in the city?

5. What is the name of the main river flowing through York?

6. Which chocolate bar gave its name to York City's football ground from 2005 to 2010?

7. To which saint is York Minster dedicated?

8. With a margin of error of ten either side, how many Archbishops of York have there been?

9. Again with a margin for error of ten either side, how many stained glass windows does the Minster have?

10. And finally with the same margin for error, how high is the central tower in metres?

Questions

York

1. **Flibbertygate.** Whipmawhopmagate was where floggings took place.

2. **They are all ghosts** that are said to haunt houses, pubs or streets in York.

3. **Waste collection.** The 'Historic Toilet Tour' covers Roman, Viking and medieval toilet facilities and habits, and graveyards are incorporated into a 'Graveyard, Coffin and Plague' tour.

4. **The Mystery Plays.** Their history can be traced back to the late 14th century.

5. **The River Ouse.** The smaller Foss also flows through the city.

6. **Kit Kat.** Bootham Crescent was renamed Kit Kat Crescent in a sponsorship deal. It was created by Rowntree's, founded in the city.

7. **Saint Peter.** Its full title is The Cathedral and Metropolitical Church of St Peter in York.

8. **97.** The first one was appointed in 627.

9. **128.** They share more than two million individual pieces of glass.

10. **60 meters.** There are 275 steps to the top of it.

Answers

Authors and Poets

1. Which famous Yorkshire poet was born in Mytholmroyd near Hebden Bridge?

2. Laurence Sterne, author of *Tristram Shandy*, lived at Shandy Hall as the curate of which north Yorkshire village?

3. Whose books include *The Lady in the Van*, *The Laying on of Hands* and *The Uncommon Reader*?

4. Which of the Brontë sisters was the eldest: Anne, Charlotte or Emily?

5. Anne, Charlotte and Emily published their books under the pseudonyms of Acton, Currer and Ellis—and what shared surname?

6. Whose novels include *Possession, Still Life* and *Babel Tower*?

7. "But at my back I always hear / Time's winged chariot hurrying near / And yonder all before us lie / Deserts of vast eternity." Which Yorkshire-born poet wrote these lines?

8. Which Barnsley-born writer wrote the novel *A Kestrel for a Knave*?

9. Playwright Alan Ayckbourn premiered all but a few of his 70-plus plays in the theatre of which Yorkshire town?

10. Who was the last Yorkshire-born author to win the Booker Prize, with a book called *The Ghost Road*?

Questions

Authors and Poets

1. **Ted Hughes.** The house on Aspinall Street where he was born has a plaque to commemorate him.

2. **Coxwold.** The house is now owned by the Laurence Sterne Trust.

3. **Alan Bennett.** He was born in Leeds and is perhaps the most quintessentially Yorkshire of all modern writers.

4. **Charlotte.** She was born in 1816, Emily in 1818, and Anne in 1820.

5. **Bell.** They chose their names because they feared they would not be taken seriously enough if they published as women.

6. **A S Byatt.** She was born in Sheffield.

7. **Andrew Marvell.** They are from 'To His Coy Mistress'. Marvell was born in Winstead-in-Holderness near Hull.

8. **Barry Hines.** His book was later turned into the award-winning Ken Loach film *Kes*.

9. **Scarborough.** Ayckbourn was artistic director there for nearly 40 years.

10. **Pat Barker.** She was born in Thornaby-on-Tees and won the prize in 1995.

Answers

Dialect and Sayings

1. What does 'baht 'at" mean in the popular song and unofficial Yorkshire anthem 'On Ilkley Moor Baht 'At'?

2. What does the clichéd Yorkshire phrase of 'eeh by gum' actually mean?

3. What is a barm pot?

4. What does 'Put wood in 'hole' mean?

5. What does 'atwixt' mean?

6. The unofficial Yorkshire motto contains the line "If ever thou does owt fer nowt, allus do it fer thissen." What does it mean?

7. If you cob, lace, pawse or wang something, what are you doing?

8. Complete this Yorkshire saying: "You can tell a Yorkshireman but…"

9. … And this rather unflattering one: "Yorkshire born and Yorkshire bred, strong…"

10. When a shepherd says 'Yan, tan, tethera', what is he doing?

Dialect and Sayings

1. **Without a hat.** The song is about a man who goes out on the moor without a hat on—which as anyone who has been there can attest, is rarely a good idea.

2. **By God.** It is what's known as a 'minced oath'—one that can be said in front of the children without wishing to properly swear.

3. **A daft or foolish person.** The derivation is unknown, but it probably refers to the barm cake.

4. **Shut the door.** It was more commonly used when fires were used to heat rooms, and less in these days of central heating.

5. **Always.**

6. **If you ever do anything for nothing, do it for yourself.** The preceding lines of the motto are "Ear all, see all, say nowt. Eat all, sup all, pay nowt."

7. **Hitting it.** Yorkshire dialect has dozens of synonyms for striking.

8. **You can't tell him much.**

9. **In the arm and weak in the head.**

10. **Counting sheep.** Yan is one, tan is two and tethera is three. It is fading from use, however.

Answers

The Great Outdoors

1. What is Yorkshire's highest mountain?

2. What are the names of Yorkshire's Three Peaks?

3. What is Yorkshire's largest freshwater lake?

4. Approximately how many miles of dry stone walls are there in Yorkshire: 13,900 miles, 18,900 miles or 23,900 miles?

5. Which is the largest National Park: the Yorkshire Dales, the North York Moors or the Peak District?

6. What is the name of the Moor that at 454m up is the highest point in the North York Moors?

7. Which waterfall has England's longest unbroken drop?

8. Where in Yorkshire is the finishing point of the famous Coast to Coast walk, as devised by Alfred Wainwright?

9. The longest river entirely within Yorkshire is 73 miles or 118 km long. What is it called?

10. What links Top Sink, the Borehole and Cow Pot?

Questions

The Great Outdoors

1. **Mickle Fell.** It is 788m or 2,585ft high. It is just inside the Yorkshire border in the north Pennines.

2. **Whernside, Ingleborough and Pen-y-ghent.**
   They are joined together in a classic walk, usually started at Horton-in-Ribblesdale.

3. **Hornsea Mere.** It is two miles from end-to-end and has a surface area of about 2 square kilometres.

4. **18,900 miles.** England as a whole has about 70,000 miles worth.

5. **The Yorkshire Dales.** It covers 685 square miles, more than the Peak District (555 square miles) and the North York Moors (554 square miles).

6. **Urra Moor.** The actual summit is Round Hill.

7. **Hardraw Force.** It is in Wensleydale and drops about 30 metres.

8. **Robin Hood's Bay.** The other end of the 190 mile walk is St Bees in Cumbria.

9. **River Ure.** It runs from Abbotside Common into the River Ouse north west of York.

10. **They are all names of entrances to the Ease Gill system of caves.** It is the longest cave network in the UK.

Answers

Houses and Gardens

1. Which medieval manor house near Ripon was the inspiration for Charlotte Brontë's *Jane Eyre*?

2. Which hall near Driffield has been lived in by the same family line since the 16th century?

3. What is the name of the Arts and Crafts style home that is now the headquarters of the National Trust in Yorkshire?

4. Sewerby Hall is situated near which popular seaside resort?

5. Which York house is supposedly haunted by ghosts of Roman legionaries?

6. When Yorkshire hosted the ceremonial start of the Tour de France in 2014, from the grounds of which stately home did it start?

7. What are the Royal Horticultural Society gardens near Harrogate called?

8. The Constable Burton gardens near Leyburn host an annual festival of which flower?

9. The Yorkshire Lavender Garden and Farm is situated in which hill range?

10. Within the grounds of which country estate can you find the Yorkshire Arboretum?

Houses and Gardens

1. **Norton Conyers.** Brontë visited in 1839 and an old staircase up to the attic was rediscovered in 2004.

2. **Burton Agnes Hall.** Parts of the estate date back to the 12th century.

3. **Goddards.** It was built for Noel Goddard Terry, grandson of the company's founder.

4. **Bridlington.** It attracts around 150,000 visitors a year.

5. **Treasurer's House.** It was the home of the treasurers of nearby York Minster until the 16th century.

6. **Harewood House.** Near Leeds. The stage ran to Harrogate.

7. **Harlow Carr.** One of four gardens run by the RHS.

8. **Tulips.** Gardeners there plant about 6,000 bulbs a year.

9. **The Howardian Hills.** It is near the village of Terrington.

10. **Castle Howard.** It is one of the country's most important collections after Kew.

Answers

Art

1. Bradford-born David Hockney is one of the UK's most renowned living artists. In which east Yorkshire town does he live and work?

2. And where in Bradford are many of his paintings on permanent display?

3. Who is the landscape artist based in Holmfirth who presented a long-running TV series on painting through the 1990s?

4. Which acclaimed sculptor has been honoured with a gallery in her name in Wakefield?

5. Who is the Castleford-born sculptor whose work was much inspired by his home county?

6. And which third renowned Yorkshire-born sculptor's work includes a 'Both Arms' sculpture on Leeds' Millennium Square?

7. Which famously shocking Young British Artist, while born and living in the south, grew up in Leeds and studied at its College of Art?

8. Which 19th century painter, born and buried in Leeds, was particularly renowned for night-time landscapes?

9. What popular collection of art between Wakefield and Barnsley can fairly claim to be the country's largest in space terms?

10. Which great painter of light was so inspired by Yorkshire that he has a dedicated trail named after him?

Questions

Art

1. **Bridlington.** Many of his paintings draw on the countryside around it.

2. **Salts Mill at Saltaire.** Once the world's largest industrial building, Salts Mill was converted for its current use in the late 1980s.

3. **Ashley Jackson.** Many of his paintings are inspired by the moors around Holmfirth.

4. **Barbara Hepworth.** The Hepworth was the largest purpose-built gallery in half a century when it opened in 2011.

5. **Henry Moore.** The Henry Moore Institute in Leeds was set up by his charitable foundation.

6. **Kenneth Armitage.** He was born in the city and studied at its College of Art.

7. **Damien Hirst.** He is now the UK's richest living artist.

8. **John Atkinson Grimshaw.** Many of his paintings are industrial or cityscapes.

9. **Yorkshire Sculpture Park.** It was voted Yorkshire's best tourist attraction in a 2011 poll.

10. **JMW Turner.** The Welcome to Yorkshire tourist board has produced a map of some places he is known to have visited.

Answers

Leeds

1. Where does Leeds rank on the list of the UK's largest cities and towns, as measured by population?

2. What is the name of the river that runs through Leeds?

3. What is the word, thought to derive from an old name for Leeds, that is used for people from the city?

4. Three major sports clubs play at Headingley in north west Leeds. Who are they?

5. The Latin motto on Leeds' coat of arms is 'Pro Rege et Lege'. What does it mean?

6. Which high-rise city landmark was named best tall building in the world in an architectural award in 2010?

7. Who designed Leeds Town Hall?

8. What major UK retail business started life on Kirkgate Market in 1884?

9. City Square in Leeds has statues of four famous local men. Can you name two of them?

10. Based on the Met Office's 30 year averages, roughly how much rainfall does Leeds get a year: 50cm, 100cm or 150cm?

Questions

Leeds

1. **Third.** Only London and Birmingham are home to more people.

2. **The River Aire.** It runs for around 70 miles in all, from Malham Tarn to the River Ouse near Goole.

3. **Loiners.** Loidis was an early name for the city, though some think the name might have derived from its lanes or 'loins'.

4. **Yorkshire Cricket Club, Leeds Rhinos rugby league club and Leeds Carnegie rugby union club.**

5. **For King and the Law.** The coat of arms also features owls, stars and a fleece.

6. **Broadcasting Place.** It is home to parts of Leeds Metropolitan University.

7. **Cuthbert Brodrick.** It was opened in 1858.

8. **Marks & Spencer.** Michael Marks set up his first stall there before joining forces with Tom Spencer.

9. **Joseph Priestley, John Harrison, James Watt & Walter Hook.**

10. **100cm.** The city gets at least 1mm of rain on 152 days of the year.

Answers

Transport

Leeds

1. What is the special claim to fame of the Middleton Railway in Hunslet in south Leeds?

2. The North Yorkshire Moors Railway is the busiest heritage rail line in the country. What are the stations at either end of the 18 mile line?

3. The highest point of any motorway in England is at Windy Hill near Saddleworth Moor. Which motorway is it on?

4. What is the name of the road in the North York Moors that is usually considered the steepest in the UK, with gradients reaching 1 in 3?

5. What is the name of the longest canal tunnel in England?

6. Which Yorkshire city is served by a tram service?

7. Where is Yorkshire's busiest train station, as measured by passenger traffic?

8. And again measured in traffic terms, which is Yorkshire's busiest airport?

9. Where in Yorkshire is the oldest cable-hauled tramway in the UK?

10. Who was the man dubbed the 'Railway King' who first brought the railway to York and many other places in Yorkshire?

Questions

Transport

1. **It is the world's longest continually running railway.** It was build as a waggonway in 1758 and is now a preserved steam line.

2. **Pickering and Whitby.** The line was reclaimed by volunteers after it was shut in the Beeching reforms of the 1960s.

3. **The M62.** It is at 372m or 1,220ft.

4. **Rosedale Chimney Bank.** It is so steep that it has a notice at the bottom advising cyclists to dismount.

5. **Standedge.** It is on the Huddersfield Narrow Canal and runs for more than 3 miles.

6. **Sheffield.** It opened in 1994 and serves 48 stations around the city.

7. **Leeds.** About 26.2 million people started or finished a journey there in 2013. The next busiest is Sheffield (8.6 million).

8. **Leeds Bradford.** It served 3.3 million passengers in 2013.

9. **Shipley Glen.** It was built in 1895 to link the Shipley Glen beauty spot to Saltaire.

10. **George Hudson.** A road near York station is named in his honour.

Answers

Cricket

1. Which batsman has scored the most career runs for Yorkshire CC?

2. And which bowler has taken the most wickets?

3. A Yorkshireman holds the world record for the best ever first-class bowling figures of 10 wickets for 10 runs. Who is he?

4. Who was Yorkshire's first ever overseas player?

5. Up to the end of the 2013 season, how many times have Yorkshire won England's County Championship?

6. The highest ever single innings score for Yorkshire is 341. Who scored it?

7. Which Yorkshireman was the first ever cricketer to take 300 wickets in Test matches?

8. Which cricketing Yorkshireman is commemorated by a statue in his home town of Barnsley?

9. Who was often nicknamed GLY or Greatest Living Yorkshireman by his teammates?

10. Three Yorkshiremen have taken hat-tricks for England in Test matches since 1999. Who are they?

Cricket

1. **Herbert Sutcliffe.** He scored 38,558 runs, including 12 centuries. In all first-class cricket, he is sixth on the all-time list.

2. **Wilfred Rhodes.** He took 3,597 wickets for the club. His total first-class wickets tally of 4,204 is the world's highest ever.

3. **Hedley Verity.** He achieved the feat against Nottinghamshire in 1932.

4. **Sachin Tendulkar of India.** He joined for the 1992 season.

5. **32**. It includes seven titles in the 1930s and six in the 1960s.

6. **George Hirst, against Leicestershire in 1905.** Darren Lehmann just missed the record when he scored 339 against Durham in 2006.

7. **Fred Trueman.** He took 307 in all, at an average of 21.57.

8. **Dickie Bird.** As a player he made only 93 first-class appearances, but as an umpire he stood in 66 Test matches.

9. **Geoffrey Boycott.** He scored 41,051 runs as a player, before going on to a career in commentary.

10. **Darren Gough, against Australia in 1999; Matthew Hoggard, against West Indies in 2004 and Ryan Sidebottom, against New Zealand in 2008.**

Answers

General Knowledge 2

1. Seven places in Yorkshire are officially designated as cities by royal charter. Can you name all seven?

2. What do these words have in common: Booze, Crackpot and Idle?

3. Allowing half a million leeway on either side, how many million acres does the historic county of Yorkshire cover?

4. How many outer petals does the Yorkshire white rose have?

5. The Great Yorkshire Bike Ride runs for 70 miles between which two towns?

6. Which of these local authorities has the smallest population in Yorkshire: Craven, Hambleton or Richmondshire?

7. What is the most easterly inhabited point of Yorkshire?

8. And what is the most westerly inhabited point?

9. Yorkshire has ten universities. Can you name at least five?

10. A Yorkshire village has the longest single-word place name in England, with letters and two hyphens. Where is it?

Questions

General Knowledge 2

1. **York, Leeds, Hull, Wakefield, Sheffield, Bradford and Ripon.**

2. **They are all place names in Yorkshire.** Booze is in Arkengarthdale, Crackpot in Swaledale and Idle near Bradford.

3. **3.8 million.** Yorkshiremen are fond of saying that the county has more acres than the Bible has letters (3.6 million).

4. **Five.** The rose is first thought to have been used as an emblem by the Duke of York's men in the 14th century.

5. **Wetherby and Filey.** The Ride started in 1983 and now attracts around 2,000 people a year.

6. **Richmondshire.** The last Census put its population at 51,000 people.

7. **Kilnsea.** It is on Spurn Head, across the Mouth of the Humber from Grimsby.

8. **Low Bentham.** It is very close to the border with Cumbria.

9. **Bradford, Huddersfield, Hull, Leeds, Leeds Metropolitan, Sheffield, Sheffield Hallam, Teesside, York and York St John.**

10. **Sutton-under-Whitestonecliffe.** It is close to Thirsk.

Answers

Museums and Attractions

1. Which national museum was opened in York in 1975?

2. And which national museum is housed in Bradford?

3. What museum will you find on the site of the former Caphouse Colliery near Wakefield?

4. Yorkshire has museums dedicated to all these things but one: fairgrounds, trolleybuses, lawnmowers and toys. Which?

5. Where in the Dales is the Dales Countryside Museum?

6. North Yorkshire has the country's oldest visitor attraction, opened in 1630. What is it called?

7. What gaming phenomenon has its own activity park at the Lightwater Valley centre?

8. What is the most popular paid-for visitor attraction in the county, with around 1.4 million visitors a year?

9. Which two places in Yorkshire are designated World Heritage Sites?

10. What is the name of the national children's museum in Halifax?

Questions

Museums and Attractions

1. **The National Railway Museum.** It attracts nearly one million visitors a year.

2. **The National Media Museum.** Its collections have some 3.5 million items.

3. **The National Coal Mining Museum.** It was formerly the Yorkshire Mining Museum.

4. **Lawnmowers.** The museums of fairgrounds and trolleybuses are in Sheffield, and of toys in Ilkley. The lawnmower museum is in Southport.

5. **Hawes**. It is open all year except January.

6. **Mother Shipton's Cave**. It commemorates a famous Yorkshire witch and has a so-called Petrifying Well.

7. **Angry Birds.** It is the UK's first – but maybe not the last – such park.

8. **Flamingo Land.** The theme park and zoo gets nearly twice as many visitors as the next most popular attraction, York Minster.

9. **Saltaire and Studley Royal Park**. Saltaire is a Victorian model town and Studley Royal Park houses the ruins of Fountains Abbey.

10. **Eureka.** It opened in 1992.

Answers

Buildings

1. The highest pub in the UK is along the Pennine Way in Swaledale in the Yorkshire Dales. What is it called?

2. Where is the Piece Hall, once a vital part of Yorkshire's wool and cotton industries?

3. Which skyscraping building is the highest in Yorkshire?

4. Which is the largest shopping centre in Yorkshire: Trinity in Leeds, Merrion in Leeds or Meadowhall in Sheffield?

5. Which artistic Yorkshire building borrows its name from Granada in Spain?

6. What is the name of the building in Leeds that was once the world's largest wool mill?

7. For what is the Parsonage at Haworth best known?

8. In 2010 archaeologists found the remains of the oldest what near Scarborough, believed to be about 10,500 years old?

9. York Minster is one of five Church of England cathedrals in Yorkshire. Can you name two of the other four?

10. And apart from York Mister, there are eight Minsters still open for worship in Yorkshire. Can you name three?

Buildings

1. **The Tan Hill Inn**. It is 528m or 1,730ft above sea level and is frequently cut off in the winter.

2. **Halifax.** It was a major trading centre in the industries. The building is being redeveloped.

3. **Bridgewater Place in Leeds.** It is nicknamed by some locals the Dalek and reaches 112m.

4. **Meadowhall in Sheffield.** It has 1.4 million square metres of floor space.

5. **The Alhambra theatre in Bradford.** It was built in 1913, inspired by Granada's Arabic palace.

6. **Armley Mills.** It is now home to a major industrial museum.

7. **The Brontë sisters.** It is where they grew up and is now the Brontë Parsonage Museum.

8. **House.** It was 3.5 metres wide, supported by wooden posts and thatched.

9. **Bradford, Ripon, Sheffield and Wakefield.** Ripon's is the oldest.

10. **Beverley, Dewsbury, Doncaster, Halifax, Leeds, Rotherham, Stonegrave and St Gregory's Minster in Kirkdale.**

Answers

The Ridings

1. The system of Ridings is based on the Danish word 'thridding', meaning what?

2. There is a North, West and East Riding but no South—yet there is a fourth entity of Yorkshire. What is it?

3. What is the name of the author who wrote a novel called *South Riding*, later made into a BBC series?

4. What is the county town of the old East Riding?

5. And what was the county town of the old North Riding?

6. And, finally, of the old West Riding?

7. What is the name for the subdivision of Ridings, similar to the Anglo-Saxon system of Hundreds?

8. Which river forms the natural border between the East and North Ridings?

9. The city of Ripon is at the centre of Yorkshire, but which Riding is it in?

10. Which area, close to Yorkshire, was the only other significant one to have a system of Ridings?

Questions

The Ridings

1. **A third.** The division of Yorkshire in this way was devised by the Vikings when they invaded.

2. **York**. It was given self-governance by the corporation of the city.

3. **Winifred Holtby.** She was born in Rudston in east Yorkshire.

4. **Beverley.**

5. **Northallerton.**

6. **Wakefield.**

7. **Wapentakes.** The three Yorkshire Ridings shared about 40 wapentakes.

8. **The River Derwent.** The River Ouse does the same along much of the border between the North and West Ridings.

9. **West Riding.** It sits close by the border-defining river.

10. **Lindsey / Lincolnshire.** It had north, south and west Ridings.

Answers

Famous People 2

1. Who was the saint who was the founding abbess of Whitby Abbey?

2. Who is the Northallerton-born mountaineer who became the first British man to climb all of the world's mountains higher than 8,000m?

3. Which ex-athletic Olympian was named the Yorkshire Man of the Year at the Yorkshire Awards in 2012?

4. Which female novelist shares her surname with one of Yorkshire's biggest towns?

5. Which one of the six members of Monty Python was born in Yorkshire?

6. Who was the Dewsbury-born female politician best known for speaking to, rather than with, the House of Commons?

7. Todmorden-born John Cockcroft was one of a pair of scientists who received the Nobel Prize for Physics in 1951. For what achievement?

8. Which of these three composers was NOT born in Yorkshire: John Barry, Benjamin Britten or Frederick Delius?

9. A Yorkshire-born man is given much of the credit for abolishing slavery. Who is he?

10. Who was the Foulby-born man who was the first to work out a way to calculate precise longitude?

Questions

Famous People 2

1. **Saint Hilda.** She was abbess from 657 until her death around 20 years later.

2. **Alan Hinkes.** He climbed them between 1987 and 2005.

3. **Sebastian Coe.** He was born in London but grew up in Sheffield, and was chair of the organizing committee for the 2012 Games.

4. **Barbara Taylor Bradford.** She was born in Leeds as Barbara Taylor and added her husband's name when she married.

5. **Michael Palin**. He was born in the Broomhill area of Sheffield.

6. **Betty Boothroyd.** She remains the only female Speaker of the House of Commons.

7. **Splitting the atom.**

8. **Benjamin Britten.** Barry was born in York and Delius in Bradford.

9. **William Wilberforce**. Slavery was officially abolished in law in 1833 just days before he died.

10. **John Harrison.** He achieved it in the 18th century via a marine chronometer that allowed seafarers to keep real time.

Answers

Sheffield

1. The River Sheaf that gives Sheffield its name is a tributary of which larger river?

2. Sheffield Wednesday wasn't actually a football club when it was originally founded. What sport did it play?

3. Of what living thing does Sheffield claim to have more of than any other city in Europe?

4. What was the name of the sports stadium in the city that was demolished in 2014?

5. How many MPs does Sheffield have?

6. At the 2011 Census, what was the approximate population of Sheffield: 350,000, 550,000 or 750,000?

7. Sheffield is referenced in Geoffrey Chaucer's *The Canterbury Tales*, when a man from there is mentioned to be holding what implement?

8. Which sport's world championships has Sheffield hosted since 1977?

9. What two places in Sheffield are named after businessman and Lord Mayor, John Graves?

10. Outside Sheffield's Town Hall is the city's 'Walk of Fame'—plaques set into the pavement in tribute to local legends. Two of them are dedicated to music acts. Which?

Questions

Sheffield

1. **The River Don**. It runs 70 miles from the Pennines to the Ouse near Goole.

2. **Cricket.** It was founded in 1820, and the football team of the same name didn't play its first match until 1868.

3. **Trees.** The city council estimates that it has more than two million.

4. **The Don Valley Stadium.** It was built in 1991.

5. **Six.** The constituencies are Attercliffe, Brightside, Central, Hallam, Heeley and Hillsborough.

6. **550,000.** The total was 7.5% up on the previous Census in 2001.

7. **A whittle or knife.** Sheffield already had a strong reputation for cutlery manufacture by the 14th century.

8. **Snooker.** The championships are held at the Crucible Theatre each spring.

9. **Graves Park and Graves Art Gallery.** Graves also donated much of his art collection to the gallery.

10. **Def Leppard and Joe Cocker.** Def Leppard played their first gig at Sheffield's Westfield school in 1978.

Answers

Name the place

Name the Yorkshire towns with the help of these cryptic clues.

1. Sharp stem.

2. Hair-raising device.

3. A knock to the surface.

4. A crowded car.

5. Knight, Craven, Mitchell or Callard.

6. Kept hopping from foot to foot.

7. Fortified building by a shallow river.

8. Home of the bear.

9. Climate forecasting insect.

10. Put into order.

Questions

Name the place

1. Thorne.

2. Acomb.

3. Dent.

4. Fulford.

5. Beverley.

6. Skipton.

7. Castleford.

8. Pudsey.

9. Wetherby.

10. Settle.

Answers

Music

1. Which Yorkshire song was reputedly composed by a church choir from Halifax on a day out?

2. Which English composer, renowned for his film scores in particular, was born in York and was named a Freeman of the city in 2002?

3. Which operatic soprano is the most famous daughter of the town of Thorne near Doncaster?

4. Which city's renowned music venues include the Corporation, Leadmill and Plug?

5. What is the name of the Yorkshire ballad that was popularised by Paul Simon and Art Garfunkel?

6. Beverley, Whitby and Otley all host festivals celebrating what style of music?

7. Which leading Britpop group was formed in Sheffield in 1978 but only found fame in the Britpop era of the 1990s?

8. Which member of the Spice Girls was born and raised in Leeds?

9. What do Brighouse & Rastrick, Carlton Main and Black Dyke have in common?

10. A Heckmondwike-born musician popularised the sight-singing system of Do-re-mi-fa-so-la-ti-do? Who?

Questions

Music

1. **'On Ilkley Moor Baht 'At'.** The group found themselves inappropriately dressed for the weather on their visit.

2. **John Barry.** His work was partly inspired by his father, who was a cinema projectionist in the city.

3. **Lesley Garrett.** She lived in Thorne until she joined the Royal Academy of Music.

4. **Sheffield.** Many big bands played some of their earliest gigs there.

5. **Scarborough Fair.** They recorded it in 1966, but versions of the song can be traced back to the 17th century.

6. **Folk.** Yorkshire has a very long history of folk songs and clubs.

7. **Pulp.** Many of their songs are inspired by growing up in the city.

8. **Mel B.** She was otherwise known as Scary Spice.

9. **They are all bands that have won the Yorkshire Brass Band Championships in recent years.** The Championships are held at St George's Hall in Bradford each year.

10. **John Curwen.** He was a minister who was prompted to develop the method while teaching Sunday school children.

Answers

Industry

1. Harry Brearley was the pioneer of which important Yorkshire industrial output?

2. Before they were decimated in the mid 1980s, how many collieries did Yorkshire have: 20, 40 or 60?

3. Now Yorkshire has just two working coal mines. Can you name either of them?

4. What is the name of the famous industrialist who created the 'model' industrial town of Saltaire near Bradford?

5. Which famous canal was built to serve the industry of Saltaire and other growing fast-growing Yorkshire mill towns?

6. What was the bright invention of Percy Shaw, who lived his whole life in Halifax?

7. Leeds ironmonger James Henry Atkinson patented a household invention called the Little Nipper. What was it?

8. What was the mining industry that fuelled massive growth in the population of the Rosedale valley in the second half of the 19th century?

9. What is the name of the gemstone that Whitby helped make famous?

10. Why do pub-goers have reason to be grateful to 18th century Barnsley-born inventor Joseph Bramah?

Questions

Industry

1. **Stainless steel.** At its peak, Sheffield had several hundred steel furnaces, and it is still widely known as 'Steel City'.

2. **60.** The heaviest concentration was in the Wakefield area.

3. **Hatfield and Kellingley.** Both are frequently under threat of closure. Another, Maltby, closed in 2013.

4. **Titus Salt.** Unlike most previous mill towns, it was equipped with facilities including running water, hospital, library and park.

5. **The Leeds to Liverpool Canal.** At 127 miles it is the longest single waterway canal in the UK.

6. **Cat's eyes.** He patented his invention in 1934.

7. **A mousetrap.** The name survives today.

8. **Iron.** The mines there were exhausted in the 1920s.

9. **Jet.** The mining and crafting of Whitby jet once employed several thousand people in the town.

10. **Because he invented the beer pump.** Among his many other inventions was the hydraulic press.

Answers

Sport

1. Which of Yorkshire's rugby league clubs has won the sport's Championship the most times?

2. Which rugby league team is known as the Flat Cappers?

3. What do Moortown, Ganton and Lindrick golf courses have in common?

4. Which Yorkshire-born brothers won gold and bronze at the 2012 London Olympics – in the same event?

5. Three more Yorkshire-born athletes won gold at the London Olympics. Can you name one of them?

6. And which Yorkshire-born cyclist won Team GB's first medal of the London Olympics?

7. What would you be watching if you saw the Stingrays play the Steelers?

8. What sporting event is played out on Whernside, Ingleborough and Pen-y-ghent each April?

9. The game of rugby officially split into two codes in 1895 when clubs from Yorkshire and Lancashire agreed a breakaway at a meeting at the George Hotel. In which town is that?

10. In what ancient throwing sport, still played competitively in Yorkshire, should you aim for a hob and throw a ringer?

Questions

Sport

1. **Leeds.** They have nine victories up to the 2013 season, including five between 2007 and 2012.

2. **Featherstone Rovers.** It gained its name from the days when just about every one of the club's working class supporters wore one.

3. **They have all hosted golf's Ryder Cup.** Moortown had it in 1929 Ganton in 1949 and Lindrick in 1957.

4. **Alistair and Jonathan Brownlee.** Alistair won gold in the triathlon and Jonathan bronze. Horsforth has a pub called the Brownlee Arms in their honour.

5. **Jessica Ennis (heptathlon, born in Sheffield); Nicola Adams (boxing, Leeds); and Luke Campbell (boxing, Hull).**

6. **Lizzie Armitstead.** She was born in Otley winning silver in the women's road race (& gold in the 2014 Commonwealth Games).

7. **Ice hockey.** Hull's team is the Stingrays and Sheffield's is the Steelers.

8. **The Three Peaks fell race**. It covers 24 miles and starts and finishes in Horton-in-Ribblesdale.

9. **Huddersfield.** There is a plaque outside to commemorate the event.

10. **Quoits.** A hob is the pin over which a quoit is thrown, and a ringer is one that has landed on the hob.

Answers

Hull

1. Who is the most famous former employee of the Brynmor Jones Library at Hull University?

2. Who was the Hull-born woman who was first to fly solo from England to Australia?

3. Hull is the only city in the country to have its own telephone operating company, and as a result its phone boxes are a different colour to the usual red. What colour are they?

4. Which infamous ship was built in Hull and lost in the Pacific in the late 1780s?

5. What is the name for people from Hull?

6. What designated UK city status is Hull enjoying in 2017?

7. What, in Hull, is the Land of Green Ginger?

8. Ferries run from Hull to a city in Holland and a city in Belgium. What are they?

9. Which of Hull's pubs played a major part in the Civil War as the place where the decision was taken to refuse Charles I admission to the city?

10. Which famous fictional adventurer set sail from Hull for far-off lands in 1651?

Hull

1. **Philip Larkin**. He was born in Coventry but moved to Hull in 1955 remaining there until he died in 1985.

2. **Amy Johnson.** There is a statue commemorating her in Hull.

3. **White / cream.** Hull proudly uses this point of difference as a symbol of its independence.

4. **HMS Bounty.** It was sailed by Captain Bligh and subject to a mutiny in the Pacific.

5. **Hullensians.** It is also the name of a rugby club in the city.

6. **City of Culture.** The honour is awarded by the Department for Culture, Media and Sport.

7. **A street.** There are several competing theories for the derivation of its name.

8. **Rotterdam in Holland and Zeebrugge in Belgium.**

9. **The Olde White Harte.** The room where the decision was made is now called the 'Plotting Parlour'.

10. **Robinson Crusoe**. Author Daniel Defoe also had his title hero born in York.

Answers

Animals

1. What kind of creature was Huddersfield Ben?

2. Where could you see penning, singling and shedding?

3. Which major Yorkshire-born reformist was a co-founder of the Royal Society for the Prevention of Cruelty to Animals?

4. What animal attraction can you find just south east of Doncaster?

5. Yorkshire has nine racecourses. Can you name at least five?

6. In what year was the major outbreak of foot and mouth disease that resulted in the forced slaughter of some half a million farm animals in Yorkshire?

7. Which classic animal-based TV series is adapted from a story originally set in Yorkshire?

8. What do Bedale, Bilsdale, Sinnington and Zetland have in common?

9. What animals would you be watching if you were at the Cock o' the North?

10. What type of bird tops the RSPB's annual Birdwatch survey of the most popular in Yorkshire?

Questions

Animals

1. **A Yorkshire Terrier dog.** He is usually reckoned to be the sire of the breed, which was often used as a ratting dog in Yorkshire mills.

2. **A sheep dog trial.** Penning is the act of herding sheep into their enclosure, and singling and shedding are separating one or several sheep from a pack.

3. **William Wilberforce.** He is better known for his key role in abolishing slavery, but was one of a group of founders who launched the charity in 1824.

4. **Yorkshire Wildlife Park.** It gets around 300,000 visitors a year.

5. **Beverley, Catterick, Doncaster, Pontefract, Redcar, Ripon, Thirsk, Wetherby and York.**

6. **2001.** Yorkshire had well over 100 recorded instances of the disease.

7. **Lassie.** Its creator, Eric Mowbray Knight, was born in Menston and set his original stories in west Yorkshire.

8. **They are all names of hunts.** Fox hunting was banned in the UK in 2005 but its traditions remain very popular in rural Yorkshire.

9. **Horses.** It is the name for the prestigious annual showjumping championships at the Great Yorkshire Show.

10. **House sparrow.** The blue tit and starling are also common.

Answers

The Coast

1. The Yorkshire coastline touches two of the regions on the shipping forecast. What are they?

2. And in which adjacent shipping forecast region, 60 miles off the Yorkshire coast, was the county's biggest ever earthquake in 1931, causing damage in Filey in particular?

3. Where is Yorkshire's sole remaining seaside pier?

4. What is the name of the town from which the Humber Bridge leaves Yorkshire?

5. Where on the Yorkshire coast will you find England's only mainland gannet breeding colony?

6. Which seaside town is rumoured to have a network of underground passages, used by 18th and 19th century smugglers?

7. Where on the Yorkshire coast is England's oldest surviving complete and working lighthouse?

8. Where on the coast does a Russian ship run aground in Bram Stoker's novel *Dracula*?

9. According to Visit England, how many towns or cities in England get more holiday trips a year than Scarborough?

10. Which seaside town has a coat of arms with a Latin motto translating as 'Always the bringer of good health'?

Questions

The Coast

1. **Tyne and Humber.** They are named after the estuaries.

2. **Dogger.** It measured 6.1 on the Richter Scale.

3. **Saltburn.** Piers at Hornsea, Scarborough and Withernsea have all been lost.

4. **Hessle.** At the other end is Barton-upon-Humber in Lincolnshire.

5. **Bempton Cliffs.** It is a RSPB nature reserve.

6. **Robin Hood's Bay.** Its tight streets also helped make it ideal for smuggling illicit goods from the coast.

7. **Flamborough Head.** An original lighthouse was built in 1669 but never lit, and the current one was built in 1806. It was automated in 1996.

8. **Whitby.** Bram Stoker did much of his research for the book in the town.

9. **One.** London gets around 3.8 million trips a year and Scarborough 1.3 million – well more than the next on the list, Blackpool with 1.1 million.

10. **Bridlington.** It is one of Yorkshire's longest standing seaside resorts.

Answers

Dales

1. Approximately how many people live within the Yorkshire Dales National Park: 20,000, 40,000 or 60,000?

2. Which of these towns is NOT within the Yorkshire Dales National Park: Hawes, Grassington or Kirkby Stephen?

3. In which village in the Dales can you find Gordale Scar, Janet's Foss and Water Sinks?

4. Which of these is the made-up dale: Bishopdale, Peterdale or Raydale?

5. Which small village is said to have got its name because 16 different dales lead into it?

6. What is the name of the railway line that runs through the Dales and over the Ribblehead Viaduct?

7. In what year did Yorkshire Dales soap opera Emmerdale first appear on ITV?

8. Gaping Gill, Stump Cross and White Scar are all names of what geographical feature in the Yorkshire Dales?

9. What, according to the most recent measure, are there 1,016km of within the Yorkshire Dales National Park?

10. Which dale is officially designated an Area of Outstanding Natural Beauty?

Questions

Dales

1. **20,000.** That equates to about 30 people per square mile.

2. **Kirkby Stephen.** It is a few miles from the north west boundary.

3. **Malham.** Gordale Scar is a ravine, Janet's Foss is a waterfall and Water Sinks is the area of limestone under which Malham's river disappears.

4. **Peterdale.** Bishopdale is in Richmondshire and Raydale is near Wensleydale.

5. **Thixendale.** It has a population of about 130.

6. **The Settle to Carlisle line.** It runs for 73 miles between the two towns.

7. **1972.** It is the country's second longest running soap behind Coronation Street and screened its 7,000th episode in 2014.

8. **Caves.** Limestone in the Dales makes it one of the best caving areas in the UK.

9. **Hedgerows.**

10. **Nidderdale.** It covers about 230 square miles.

Answers

TV and Film

1. Members of a Yorkshire branch of the Women's Institute provided the inspiration for the very successful *Calendar Girls* film. Which village is home to that branch?

2. Which 1990s film had an eye-catching final scene that was shot at the Shiregreen Working Men's Club in Sheffield?

3. Which Yorkshire railway line was used in the filming of the original *Railway Children* film in 1970?

4. The 1996 film *Brassed Off* is based on the true story of a brass band following a colliery closure. Which colliery is it?

5. In which village in the North York Moors national park was the TV series *Heartbeat* filmed?

6. Which long-running TV series was largely filmed in and around the small town of Holmfirth?

7. Which Yorkshire-born TV personality was born in Cudworth in 1935 grew up in Barnsley and had trials for the county cricket team with Geoffrey Boycott?

8. Which TV series was inspired by the books of James Herriot?

9. What is the title of the book by Barry Hines, set in Yorkshire's old mining areas, that was turned into a successful film?

10. In which Yorkshire stately home was much of the *Brideshead Revisited* drama series filmed?

Questions

TV and Film

1. **Rylstone.** Many of the film's scenes were shot in nearby Kettlewell.

2. **The Full Monty.** The film was completely shot in and around Sheffield, including at some of its disused steelworks.

3. **The Keighley and Worth Valley Railway.** The five-mile track was closed as a commercial venture in 1962 but soon reclaimed as a heritage steam line.

4. **Grimethorpe Colliery.** The band continues to be active more than two decades after the colliery was closed.

5. **Goathland.** The village is on the North Yorkshire Moors Railway line.

6. **Last of the Summer Wine.** The series has its own exhibition and gift shop in the town.

7. **Michael Parkinson.** He remains an avid cricket fan.

8. **All Creatures Great and Small.** Herriot had a Thirsk vet practice, which is now a tourist attraction devoted to the show.

9. **Kes.** Hines was born in Barnsley.

10. **Castle Howard.** As well as featuring in the 1981 classic series, it was also the setting for the 2008 film remake.

Answers